Celeb

ALSO AVAILABLE FROM
PRIVATE EYE · CORGI

30 YEARS OF PRIVATE EYE CARTOONS

The very best of the cartoons that have
appeared in PRIVATE EYE over the last 30 years.
£4.99

LORD GNOME'S *COMPLETE* FIB AND LIE DIET

contains the Best of Private Eye 1989 - 1991 and includes:
*Easy to understand jokes
*Delicious parodies
*Tasty cartoons
*Slimline Robert Maxwell
£4.99

These cartoon strips originally appeared in PRIVATE EYE
Published in Great Britain by Private Eye Productions Ltd,
6 Carlisle Street, London W1V 5RG,
in association with Corgi Books

© 1991 Peattie, Taylor & Warren
ISBN 0 552 13858 4

Printed in Great Britain by
The Bath Press, Bath, Avon

Corgi Books are published by Transworld Publishers Ltd,
61-63 Uxbridge Road, Ealing, London W5 5SA,
in Australia by Transworld Publishers (Australia) Pty, Ltd,
15-23 Helles Avenue, Moorebank, NSW 2170
and in New Zealand by Transworld Publishers (N.Z.) Ltd,
Cnr. Moselle and Waipareira Avenues, Henderson, Auckland

by
Charles Peattie, Mark Warren and Russell Taylor

PRIVATE EYE · CORGI

Dedication

This book is dedicated to my three ex-wives, Sandra, Rosa-Mercedes and Kelly Jo. Without their outrageous alimony demands the publication of this book and the resulting royalties would never have been necessary.

G B.
Mustique, May 1991

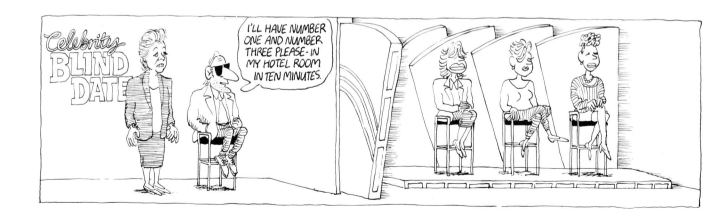

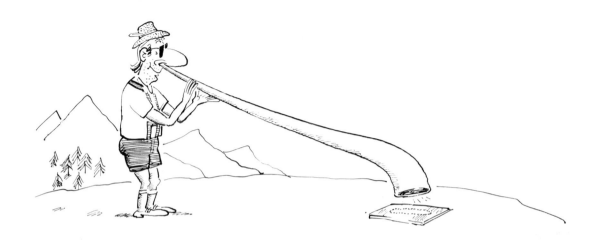

A LIFE IN THE DAY OF

Gary Bloke

Gary Bloke, international superstar and darling of the gossip columns has recently completed yet another monumentally successful world tour. While in Britain he divides his time between his Chelsea penthouse and his handsome Sussex country seat.

"I don't really get up at any particular time, it all depends on what I was doing the night before. The first thing I do when I wake up is give the bell rope above my bed a good yank, that tells Johnson, my butler, that I'm in the land of the living and needful of a good strong cuppa. There's nothing like a cup of tea to blow the cobwebs away.

Johnson's been with me almost ten years now. He's an absolute treasure — I'd be lost without him. Once I'm up and dressed — Johnson generally advises me on what shade of black to wear. I go through the papers to see what's happening in this funny old world of ours. I try not to take too much notice of what the gutter press say about me. They make most of it up as they go along. Mind you, some of it can be very hurtful. It's their obsession with my sex life, that really gets my goat. Call me old fashioned but what a man does in the privacy of his own billiard room with a group of teenage nymphets should be his own business.

Having a house in the country and a pad in town means I have to spend a lot of time travelling. No matter how rich and successful you are people like me still get stuck in traffic jams like everyone else. I hate it. I get very snappy and irritable with other drivers when that happens. My chauffeur bears the brunt of it though. The sooner he gets his private pilot's licence the better. I've had the Lear Jet for two years now but I don't even know how to switch the thing on.

Mid-morning I like to go through my fan mail. I personally make sure that everyone who writes to me gets a reply. It's common courtesy I think. When she's finished forging all the signatures my personal assistant Suzie goes over all the tax and finance matters for me. It's things like that, that make me wish I'd studied harder at school — I'm still not entirely sure where the Cayman Islands are.

Talking of abroad, it wasn't until I was forced to go and live in France as a tax exile that I realised what a true Brit I am. Sounds daft I know but it was the little things I missed — bacon and eggs, proper sausages and, above all, Branston Pickle.

I'm much happier living where I do now. It's a 26 bedroomed country house set in 25 acres of land and was built in 1851. I'd have preferred to buy a new one like Andy and Fergie but you can't have everything I suppose.

One of the most satisfying aspects of being famous is I can do lots of work for charity. Celebrity football matches, polo, clay pigeon shooting, cricket, you name it I'll have a go. Cricket's my favourite though. It's such a quintessentially English pastime. My old mate and drinking partner Ian Botham coached me, which was a fabulous experience. According to him I've got all the makings of a very useful twelfth man — whatever that means.

There's been a lot in the papers recently about my brave battle against my cocaine habit. The doctors told me that if I didn't pack it in pronto I'd end up a total physical wreck. It's been six long weeks now since I publicly vowed never to touch the stuff again and it hasn't been easy I can tell you. No-one knows what I'm going through — about four grams a week I think. Only kidding, honestly.

Of an evening I like to go to one or two parties then on to a club for a bit of r and r. I'm a real night owl, it's my body clock I guess. When I finally roll home and hit the sack I fall asleep quickly and have very vivid dreams.

13 THINGS YOU DIDN'T KNOW ABOUT GARY BLOKE

1 Gary was brought up in a 2-bedroom terrace house in Deptford and now owns property in seven countries.

2 His personal fortune is estimated at 50 million pounds.

3 His favourite dishes are Lobster à la Parisienne avec Pomme de terre Emielles and Lancashire Hot Pot — his mother's recipe.

4 The most important woman in his life is still his mum. Every year he makes a point of going to see her on her birthday at the Gate House she lives in at the end of his drive.

5 One of his biggest fans is Princess Di, "A smashing Lady — one in a million".

6 His very first guitar was a 7th birthday present from his uncle Bert.

7 He has three children, Troy, Pixie Frou Frou and

Rosedrop-Bunny petal. He owns two yachts, 'Roger' and 'Denis'.

8 The highpoint of his career was meeting Mother Teresa, "A smashing Lady — one in a million".

9 The most emotional moment of his life was seeing his youngest daughter Rosedrop-Bunny petal being born. "It was beautiful, really moving sitting there watching the miracle of birth captured on video by David Lynch. The man's a genius."

10 Gary is fanatical about his body. He travels everywhere with his personal fitness trainer in case anything heavy needs moving or lifting.

11 Despite his wild boy image Gary's idea of heaven is simple — sitting in front of a blazing log fire with a mug of cocoa and a lady friend.

12 During his recent sell-out world tour he was supported on stage by Elton John, Rod Stewart, Phil Collins and Bob Geldof. "It's fabulous having mates like that. I'd overindulged so much in the dressing room before there was no way I could stand up on my own."

13 When he dies he would like to be

remembered by a statue in London or a boulevard named after him in Los Angeles.

Bob Geldof, George Michael, David Bowie and yours truly giving it our all at Live Aid.

TO:
THE EDITOR OF THE
EVENING STANDARD

WHY I LIVE IN CHELSEA, SUSSEX, NEW YORK,
L.A., MONACO, RHODES AND BARBADOS.

Because I'm stinking rich.
Get one of your sub-editors to pad
it out. Hope it's Okay.

Cheers,
Gary

P.S. Re your enquiry about me writing a piece
for your regular 'Me and My Health' column.
You've got to be joking surely.

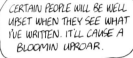

I KNOW. LET'S TURN ON ALL THE LIGHTS IN THE HOUSE.

HOLD ON, GARY. HUGE GREAT MANSION LIKE THIS. IS THAT PRUDENT?

I THOUGHT WE WERE GOING TO TRY TO CONSERVE ENERGY.

OH YES.

BETTER GET JOHNSON TO DO IT.

YOUR TURN TO PULL THE BELL-ROPE.

SELINA, MY DARLING, WHAT'S ALL THIS I'VE BEEN READING ABOUT "SELINA SCOTT AND CHARLES DANCE SAY GOOD LOOKS CAN BE A HINDRANCE IN ONE'S CAREER."?

IT'S TRUE, GARY. I'VE FOUND BEING ATTRACTIVE AN ENORMOUS DRAWBACK ON NUMEROUS OCCASIONS. PEOPLE SEE A GLAMOROUS SEXY WOMAN NOT A SUCCESSFUL TV PRESENTER.

I SOMETIMES WISH I WAS A DUMPY OLD PLAIN JANE. I'D STILL BE WHERE I AM TODAY, I'M SURE.

AT ONE OF MY PARTIES? NO YOU BLOODY WOULDN'T, LOVE.

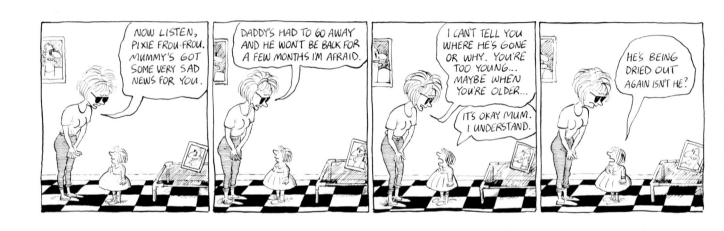